Beilstein Dictionary
German–English

Beilstein Dictionary
German–English

for the users of the
Beilstein Handbook of Organic Chemistry

Beilstein Institute Frankfurt/Main

ISBN 3-540-09378-8 Springer-Verlag, Berlin · Heidelberg · New York
ISBN 0-387-09378-8 Springer-Verlag, New York · Heidelberg · Berlin

Printing: Mercedes-Druck, Berlin

Preface

The Beilstein Dictionary (German/English) has been compiled by the scientific staff of the Beilstein Institute for Handbook users whose native language is not German. With a total of about 2,100 entries, it contains most German words occurring in the Beilstein Handbook, as well as all common abbreviations, alphabetically listed with their English equivalents.

An appended supplement (page 59 onwards) lists a series of "standard formulations" frequently used in Beilstein, together with their English translations.

It is our hope that this glossary will prove of assistance to the non German-speaking user of Beilstein, in overcoming any language difficulties which may be encountered.

The editorial staff of Beilstein

Notes for the user

The English equivalents of German words appearing in the Beilstein Handbook are chosen such that in each case the most usual translation **in the context of the Handbook of Organic Chemistry** is listed first, followed by other possibilities which can also occur **in this context.** The equivalents of a particular German word which are not relevant to this context are not included; e.g. the word "mittelständig" in a chemical text would almost invariably mean "in a middle or central position" and NOT "middle class" which is the everyday meaning of the word.

German words whose spelling is identical to the English or so similar that confusion is unlikely to arise are generally not included; e.g. the German words "Potential" and "Elektrode" are not listed. Synonyms of English words are not given when their meaning is **identical** to the word listed; e.g. German "nahe" is translated by the word "near"; the synonym "close", which is identical in meaning, is not given.

Where a German word can have several different translations according to the context in which it occurs (within the wider context of the Handbook), or where the English word given is open to misinterpretation, an explanatory note is provided in brackets; e.g. German "abhandeln" is translated as "treat", the words "a topic or subject" are given in brackets to indicate the usage of this word, which cannot, for example, mean treat a patient, or, treat a solid with a liquid etc.

Past participles and other parts of verbs which may not be immediately recognizable from the infinitive form are listed separately at the appropriate place (alphabetically); e.g. "ist" (is) will be found as well as "sein" (to be).

The preposition "to", indicating the infinitive form, is included before all English verbs. This enables the user to identify the German word immediately as a verb.

Nouns in German, as in many other languages, with the notable exception of English, are associated with a GENDER, masculine (m), feminine (f) or neuter (n), even though the noun may refer to an inanimate object or an abstract idea. The genders of all nouns included in this vocabulary are indicated by the appropriate letter in brackets behind the German word. This is not only useful for the user who has some knowledge of German but also enables immediate identification of a noun. Another feature which facilitates recognition of German nouns is that they are all invariably written with a capital letter (not just proper nouns as in English).

Most "longer" German words (usually nouns) are compound words formed by simply writing two (or occasionally more) shorter words together (to form a new idea associated with both of them), but without a space or hyphen as is usual in English.

e.g. "reaction vessel" would be written "Reaktionsgefäss" in German, i.e. "Reaktion" (reaction) plus "Gefäss" (vessel). The additional "s" or sometimes "n" between two words merely acts as a link without further significance.

In order to make such "double" nouns easier to read for users of this vocabulary who are unfamiliar with them, they are printed with a hyphen between them, e.g. "Reaktionsgefäss" is written "Reaktions-gefäss", (clearly indicating the association of ideas), although in the text of the Handbook the two words are more commonly to be found in the composite form without the hyphen. German words beginning with a modified vowel (ä, ö, ü) are to be found immediately after those beginning with the corresponding unmodified vowel. e.g. **ab** before **äb** before **ac** before **äc** etc.

The letters double 's' can be written in two ways in German, either as ss or as ß (similar to Greek beta), according to a special set of rules (which are of no interest to the non-linguist). In order to simplify matters for the non German-speaker and avoid confusion, only the ss form is used in this dictionary.

A

A. = Äthanol *(n)* ethanol

Abbau *(m)* decomposition, degradation

abdestillieren to distil (off)

aber but, however

abfangen to intercept, retain

abgeben to give off (gas etc.), release, evolve, set free

   gibt ... ab gives off (gas etc.), releases, evolves, sets free

abhandeln to treat (a topic or subject)

Abhandlung *(f)* treatise

abhängig dependent

Abhängigkeit *(f)* dependence

abheben to lift off

Abklingdauer(zeit) *(f)* decay time

abkühlen to cool (down, off)

Abkühlung *(f)* cooling (down, off)

Abkürzung *(f)* abbreviation

ablaufen to run (off), proceed (reaction, process etc.)

   läuft ... ab runs (off), proceeds (reaction, process etc.)

Abnahme *(f)* removal, decrease (pressure, conc'n etc.)

abnehmend decreasing (pressure, conc'n etc.)

Abscheidung *(f)* separation, precipitation, sequestration

Abschnitt *(m)* section, segment, portion, paragraph

Absorptions-querschnitt *(m)* absorption cross-section

abspalten eliminate, to split off

Abspaltung *(f)* elimination, splitting off

Abstand *(m)* distance, spacing, interval

abtrennen to separate (off), detach

Abtrennung *(f)* separation, detachment

Abwasser *(n)* waste water

Abwässer sewage, run-off water

abweichen to deviate, differ, vary

abweichend deviating, differing, varying

Abweichung *(f)* deviation, difference, variation

Abwesenheit *(f)* absence

Acetanhydrid *(n)* acetic anhydride

Achse *(f)* axis

acht eight

Acidität *(f)* acidity

Acn. = **Aceton** *(n)* acetone

Additions-verbindung *(f)* addition compound

Adhäsions-spannung *(f)* adhesive tension

Adipinsäure *(f)* adipic acid
adsorbieren to adsorb
Adsorptions-gleichgewicht *(n)* adsorption equilibrium
Ae. = Diäthyläther *(m)* diethyl ether
Affinität *(f)* affinity
Agenz s. Reagenz
Aggregat-zustand *(m)* state of aggregation
ähnlich similar(ly)
Akkomodations-koeffizient *(m)* accomodation coefficient
aktiv active
aktivieren to activate
Aktivierungs-energie *(f)* activation energy
Aktivitäts-koeffizient *(m)* activity coefficient
Aktivkohle *(f)* active carbon, charcoal
alkal. = alkalisch alkaline
alkoholfrei alcohol free
Alkylierung *(f)* alkylation
alle all, every
allgemein general(ly)
allmählich gradual(ly)
als than, as
  besser als better than
alt old
altern to age
Ameisensäure *(f)* formic acid
Ammoniak *(n)* ammonia
amorph amorphous
an at, on, upon
analog analogous

Analyse *(f)* analysis
ander(e) other, different
ändern to change, modify
anders otherwise, differently
Änderung *(f)* change, modification
Anfang *(m)* beginning
anfänglich initial(ly)
anfangs (anfänglich) initially
Anfangs-druck *(m)* initial pressure
Anfangs-geschwindigkeit *(f)* initial velocity
Anfangs-temperatur *(f)* initial temperature
Anfangs-wert *(m)* initial value
Angabe *(f)* statement, specification, information, data
  entgegen der Angabe contrary to the statement
angeben to state, specify, give (information)
  angegeben given, stated, specified
angenommen assumed
angeregt stimulated, excited, induced, suggested (idea etc.)
angesäuert acidified
angesehen seen, viewed, considered
angreifen to attack
  greift ... an attacks
Angriff *(m)* attack
Anionen-austauscher *(m)* anion exchanger
anisotrop anisotropic

anlagern to add (to), take up
Anlagerung *(f)* addition (to)
Anm. = **Anmerkung** *(f)* annotation, footnote
annähern to approach, approximate
annähernd approximately
Annahme *(f)* assumption, supposition
annehmen to assume, suppose
Anordnung *(f)* arrangement, order
anorganisch inorganic
anregen to stimulate, excite, induce
Anregung *(f)* stimulation, excitation, induction, suggestion (idea etc.)
anreichern to enrich
angereichert enriched
ansäuern to acidify
anschliessend subsequent(ly), following
ansehen als to consider (as), assume (to be)
ist als ... angesehen worden has been considered (as), has been assumed (to be)
Ansicht *(f)* opinion, view
entgegen der Ansicht contrary to the opinion
anstatt instead of, in place of
Anteil *(m)* part, portion, share
Antimon *(n)* antimony
anwenden to apply, use

Anwendung *(f)* application, use
Anwesenheit *(f)* presence
Anzahl *(f)* number, quantity
Anzeichen *(n)* indication, sign
Äpfelsäure *(f)* malic acid
äquimolar equimolar
äquivalent equivalent
Aräometer *(n)* areometer
Aroma-stoff *(m)* flavouring
aromatisch aromatic
Art *(f)* kind, species, type
Artikel *(m)* article, item (in Beilstein)
Asbest *(m)* asbestos
Asche *(f)* ash
assoziiert associated
at = **technische Atmosphäre** *(f)* technical atmosphere
Äthanol *(n)* ethanol
äthanol. = **äthanolisch** ethanolic, solution in ethanol
Äther *(m)* ether (diethyl ether)
äther. = **ätherisch** ethereal, essential (oils), volatile (oils)
Äthyl *(n)* ethyl
atm = **physikalische Atmosphäre** *(f)* physical (standard) atmosphere
Atom-abstand *(m)* interatomic distance
atomar atomic
Atom-gewicht *(n)* atomic weight
ätzend corrosive, etching (effect)

Ätzkali *(n)* potassium hydroxide

auch also

auf on, to, up

  auf 100° to 100°

  auf einem Träger on a support

  auf Grund because of, on account of

aufbewahren to keep, store

  beim Aufbewahren on storing

aufeinanderfolgend succesive(ly)

auffallend incident (light etc.), conspicuous

  auffallendes Licht incident light

aufführen to present, list (results etc.)

  aufgeführt presented, listed

aufgebracht introduced onto (into), brought up

Aufklärung *(f)* explanation, elucidation

Aufl. = Auflage *(f)* edition

auflösen to dissolve

  auflösend dissolving

Auflösung *(f)* dissolution

Aufnahme *(f)* uptake, assimilation, absorption

auftreten to appear, emerge

  tritt . . . auf appears

Auftritts-potential *(n)* appearance potential

aufweisen to exhibit, show

  weist . . . auf exhibits

aufzufassen to be understood (as)

aus from, out of

Ausbeute (an) *(f)* yield (of)

Ausdehnungs-koeffizient *(m)* coefficient of expansion

ausfällen to precipitate

ausfrieren to separate (concentrate) by freezing, freeze out

ausführen to carry out

Ausgabe *(f)* issue, edition (periodical etc.)

Ausgangs-material *(n)* starting material

Ausgangs-verbindung *(f)* starting compound

ausgehen von to start from

  ausgehend von starting from

ausgenommen except for

ausgeschieden separated (out), precipitated, secreted

auslösen to initiate, release

  ausgelöst initiated

Ausmass *(n)* extent

Ausnahme *(f)* exception

ausreichend sufficient(ly), enough

ausscheiden to separate (out), precipitate

  ausgeschieden separated, precipitated

Ausscheidung *(f)* separation, precipitation

ausschliessen to exclude
ausschliesslich exclusive(ly)
Ausschluss (von Feuchtigkeit, Sauerstoff etc.) *(m)* exclusion (of moisture, oxygen etc.)
ausser besides, except for
ausserdem in addition, further
Austausch *(m)* exchange

auswaschen to wash out, scrub (gases)
Ausweis *(m)* statement, record
   nach Ausweis des ... according to, as shown by
Autoklav *(m)* autoclave

B

B. = Bildung *(f)* formation
Bad *(n)* bath
bakteriell bacterial
Bakterien *(f)* bacteria
Baldrian *(m)* valerian
Band *(m)* volume
Bande *(f)* (wave)band
Barytlauge *(f)* barium hydroxide solution
Barytwasser *(n)* barium hydroxide solution
basisch basic
Basizität *(f)* basicity
Baum-wolle *(f)* cotton
Bd. = Band *(m)* volume
bebrütet incubated, hatched (eggs)
Bedeutung *(f)* meaning, significance
Bedingung *(f)* condition, requirement
befreien to free
   befreit freed

Befund *(m)* finding(s)
begrenzt limited
behandeln to treat
   beim Behandeln on, by treating (treatment)
   nach Behandlung after treatment
bei, beim on (plus present participle), concerning, at
   beim Filtrieren on filtering
   bei 50° at 50°
beide both
Beimengung *(f)* admixture, addition (of a substance)
Beispicl *(n)* example
Beitrag *(m)* contribution
beizen to corrode, cauterize (medical), stain (wood), pickle (metal)
bekannt known
belichten to expose (to light)
Belichtung *(f)* exposure to light

Bemerkung *(f)* remark
benetzbar wettable, moistenable
Benetzbarkeit *(f)* wettability
Benzin *(n)* petroleum ether, petrol, gasoline
Benzol *(n)* benzene
Benzol-ring *(m)* benzene ring
beobachten to observe
Beobachtung *(f)* observation
beraubt deprived (of)
berechnen to calculate
berechnet calculated
Berechnung *(f)* calculation
Bereich *(m)* range
bereiten to prepare
bereits already
Bereitschaft *(f)* (state of) readiness
berichtigen to correct
Berichtigung *(f)* correction
Bernsteinsäure *(f)* succinic acid
Beschaffenheit *(f)* nature, quality
beschleunigen to accelerate
Beschleunigung *(f)* acceleration
beschränken to limit
beschreiben to describe
beschrieben described
Beschuss *(m)* bombardment
besonders especially
besser better
beständig stable
Bestandteil *(m)* component
bestätigen to confirm

Bestätigung *(f)* confirmation
best(e) best (adjective)
am besten best (adverb)
bestehen to consist of, to exist
bestimmen to determine
Bestimmung *(f)* determination
bestrahlen to irradiate
Bestrahlung *(f)* irradiation
Beteiligung *(f)* participation
Betracht *(m)* consideration
in B. ziehen take into c.
in B. kommen be considered
beträchtlich considerable
Betrachtung *(f)* consideration, observation, viewing
betragen to amount to
beträgt amounts to
Betriebs-sicherheit *(f)* operational safety, plant (works) safety
Beugung *(f)* diffraction
Beurteilung *(f)* assessment, judgement
bevorzugt preferred, preferably
Beweis *(m)* evidence, proof
beweisen to prove, establish
bezeichnen to designate, name
Bezeichnung *(f)* designation, name
beziehen to obtain
sich beziehen auf to refer to, relate to
bezogen auf referred to, related to
Beziehung *(f)* relationship

Bezug (auf) *(m)* reference (to)
bezüglich referring to, with respect to, for (regarding)
Bier *(n)* beer
Bier-hefe *(f)* (brewer's) yeast, barm
bilden to form
  bildet sich is formed
Bildung *(f)* formation
Bildungs-enthalpie *(f)* enthalpy of formation
Bildungs-konstante *(f)* (equilibrium) constant of formation
Bildungs-wärme *(f)* heat of formation
Bildungs-weise *(f)* mode (method) of formation
Bimsstein *(m)* pumice (stone)
binär binary
binden to bond, bind
  gebunden bonded, bound
Bindung *(f)* bond
Bindungs-energie *(f)* bond energy, bonding energy, binding energy
Bindungs-enthalpie *(f)* enthalpy of bonding (combination)
Bindungs-moment *(n)* bond moment
Bindungs-winkel *(m)* bond angle
Binnendruck *(m)* internal pressure
bis until
bis auf up to, except for
bisweilen occasionally, sometimes
bituminös bituminous
blass pale
Blatt *(n)* leaf
Blättchen *(n)* leaflet, lamella
blau blue
Blaufärbung *(f)* blue coloration
blaugrün blue-green
bläulich bluish
  bläulichgrün bluish-green
Blausäure *(f)* hydrocyanic acid
blauviolett blue-violet
Blei *(n)* lead
bleichen to bleach, fade
Bleicherde *(f)* Fuller's earth
Blei-kathode *(f)* lead cathode
Bleiweiss *(n)* basic lead carbonate, white lead
Blei-zucker *(m)* lead acetate, sugar of lead
Blitz-licht *(n)* flash
  Blitzlicht-Photolyse *(f)* flash photolysis
Blut *(n)* blood
Blüte *(f)* flower, bloom
Bogen-licht *(n)* arc light
Bor *(n)* boron
Borsäure *(f)* boric acid
brauchbar useful, suitable
braun brown
  braungelb yellow-brown
  braunviolett brownish violet
Braunkohlen-teer *(m)* lignite (bituminous) tar

Braunstein *(m)* manganese dioxide, pyrolusite

Brechung *(f)* refraction

Brechungs-dispersion *(f)* refractive dispersion

Brechungs-index *(m)* refractive index

Brechweinstein *(m)* tartar emetic, potassium antimonyl tartrate

Breite *(f)* width

Brennbarkeit *(f)* combustibility

Brenner *(m)* burner

Brenner-abmessung *(f)* burner dimension

Brenngeschwindigkeit *(f)* rate of combustion

Brennpunkt *(m)* fire point

Brenzkatechin *(n)* (pyro)catechol

Brenzschleimsäure *(f)* pyromucic acid

Brenztraubensäure *(f)* pyruvic acid

Brenzweinsäure *(f)* pyrotartaric acid

Brom *(n)* bromine

Bromierung *(f)* bromination

Brücke *(f)* bridge

Brücken-kopf *(m)* bridge-head

Bruttoformel *(f)* empirical formula

Buchen-holz *(n)* beech wood

Buttersäure *(f)* butyric acid

Bzl. = Benzol *(n)* benzene

Bzn. = Benzin *(n)* petroleum ether

bzw. = beziehungsweise or, respectively

C

c = Konzentration *(f)* concentration

calorimetrisch calorimetric(al)-(ly)

Carbolöl *(n)* carbolic oil

Charakterisierung *(f)* characterization

chemisch chemical(ly)

Chinasäure *(f)* quinic acid

Chinhydron *(n)* quinhydrone

Chinin *(n)* quinine

Chinolin *(n)* quinoline

Chinon *(n)* quinone

Chinoxalin *(n)* quinoxaline

Chlor *(n)* chlorine

Chlorierung *(f)* chlorination

Chlor-wasserstoff *(m)* hydrogen chloride

Circular-dichroismus *(m)* circular dichroism
citronengelb lemon yellow

Citronensäure *(f)* citric acid
Coriolis-konstanten *(f)* Coriolis constants

D

D = (1) **Debye** Debye, (2) **Dichte** *(f)* density
d = **Tag** *(m)* day
dagegen in contrast, however
damit with it, with this, therewith, herewith
Dampf *(m)* vapour
Dampf-bad *(n)* steam bath
Dampf-druck *(m)* vapour pressure
   Dampfdruck-diagramm *(n)* vapour pressure diagram
   Dampfdruck-gleichung *(f)* vapour pressure equation
   Dampfdruck-kurve *(f)* vapour pressure curve
dampfförmig in the vapour state
Dampf-gemisch *(n)* vapour mixture
Dampf-phase *(f)* vapour phase
danach afterwards
daneben next to it, besides, in addition
darf may
darin in it (that, them), therein
Darreichung *(f)* presentation

Darstellung *(f)* preparation, representation
   zusammenfassende Darst. review, survey
darüber hinaus furthermore
das the, that (demonstrative pronoun), which
dass that (conjunction)
Dauer *(f)* duration, length (time)
dazu to this, thereto, in addition
Decarboxylierung *(f)* decarboxylation
Deformations-schwingung *(f)* deformation (bending) vibration
Dehydratisierung *(f)* dehydration
Dehydrierung *(f)* dehydrogenation
dem to the, to which, to whom
dementsprechend accordingly
demgemäss accordingly
den the, to the, to which, to whom
Depolarisations-grad *(m)* degree of depolarisation

17

Deprotonierung *(f)* deprotonation

der the, to the, of the, which, who, to which, to whom

derart(ig) such, of this (that) sort

Derivat *(n)* derivative

desgleichen likewise

Desinfektions-wirkung *(f)* disinfectant effect

desinfizieren do disinfect
  desinfizierend disinfecting

Destillation *(f)* distillation

destillierbar distillable

Detonations-geschwindigkeit *(f)* rate (velocity) of detonation

deutlich clear(ly)

diabetisch diabetic

diamagnetisch diamagnetic

Diazotierung *(f)* diazotization

Dichroismus *(m)* dichroism

dichroistisch dichroistic

Dichte *(f)* density

dick thick

die the, which, who

dielektrische Sättigung *(f)* dielectric saturation

dielektrischer Verlust *(m)* dielectric loss

Dielektrizitäts-konstante *(f)* dielectric constant

dienen to serve, act (as)
  dienend serving, acting (as)

dies this (that)

diesbezüglich in this respect, concerning this matter

diese this, these (that, those)

Differential-Thermoanalyse *(f)* differential thermal analysis

differentiell differential

Diffusions-geschwindigkeit *(f)* rate of diffusion

Diffusions-koeffizient *(m)* diffusion coefficient

digerieren to digest

dilatometrisch dilatometric-(al)(ly)

Dispersions-bereich *(m)* dispersion range

Diss. = Dissertation *(f)* dissertation, thesis

Dissoziations-druck *(m)* dissociation pressure

Dissoziations-energie [D (R—X)] *(f)* dissociation energy

Dissoziations-konstante *(f)* dissociation constant

Doppelbindung *(f)* double bond

Doppelbrechung *(f)* birefringence

doppelt double

Doppelverbindung *(f)* double compound

dort there

Dosis *(f)* dose

drehen to turn, rotate

Drehungs-vermögen *(n)* rotatory power, (angle of) rotation

molares Drehungsvermögen molecular rotation

spezifisches Drehungsvermögen specific rotation
drei three
drei Mal (dreimal) three times
Dreifachbindung *(f)* triple bond
dreissig thirty
dritte(r) third
(ein) Drittel *(n)* one third
Druck *(m)* pressure
Druck-abhängigkeit *(f)* pressure dependence
Druck-änderung *(f)* pressure change
Druck-fehler *(m)* misprint
Druck-ofen *(m)* pressure oven
Druck-rohr *(n)* pressure tube
[D(R—X)] = Dissoziationsenergie *(f)* dissociation energy
dunkel dark
dunkelblau dark blue
dunkelbraun dark brown

dunkelrosa dark pink
dunkelrot dark red
Dunkelheit *(f)* darkness
dünn thin
durch through, by
durch Erhitzen by heating
durchdringend penetrating
durchfallend(es) (Licht) transmitted (light)
durchführen to carry out, accomplish
Durchlässigkeit *(f)* permeability
durchleiten to conduct, pass (through)
durchscheinend transparent, translucent
Durchschlags-festigkeit *(f)* **(elektrische)** dielectric strength
Durchströmung *(f)* flow through
dürfen may
dynamisch dynamic

E

E = (1) Erstarrungspunkt *(m)* freezing (solidification) point **(2) Ergänzungswerk des Beilstein-Handbuchs** *(n)* Beilstein Supplementary Series
E. = Äthylacetat *(n)* ethyl acetate

ebenfalls as well, likewise
ebullioskopisch ebullioscopic
echt genuine
Edelgas *(n)* noble gas
Eg. = Essigsäure *(f)*, **Eisessig** *(m)* acetic acid
ehemals formerly

eher   rather, sooner
Eichung *(f)*   calibration
eigen, eigene, eigenes   (it's, one's) own, specific
Eigenschaft *(f)*   property
(sich) eignen   to be suitable
Eignung *(f)*   suitability
ein   a (an), one
  eine   a (an), one
  einem   to a (an), to one
  einen   a (an), one
  einer   to a (an), to one, of a (an), of one
  eines   of a (an), of one
einblasen   to blow in
einbringen   to introduce
eindampfen   to evaporate
eindeutig   unambiguous
einengen   to concentrate
einfach   simple
Einfluss *(m)*   influence
einfügen   to insert, fit in
  ist einzufügen   is to be inserted
eingefroren   to be frozen
Einheit *(f)*   unit
einheitlich   uniform(ly), homogeneous(ly)
Einheitlichkeit *(f)*   uniformity, homogeneity
einige   some, several
Einkristall *(m)*   single crystal
einleiten   to introduce, pass into, feed into
  beim Einleiten von . . . in   on passing . . . into

einmal, ein Mal   once
eins   one
einsäurig   mon(o)acid
einschlägig   relevant, pertinent
Einschluss-verbindung *(f)*   inclusion compound, clathrate
Einschmelz-rohr *(n)*   Carius tube, sealed tube
Einschränkung *(f)*   restriction
einstündig   for one hour
eintägig   for one day
eintragen   to introduce, record
  unter Eintragen   with introduction (of)
eintropfen   to add dropwise
Einwirkung *(f)*   action, influence
einzig   only, single, unique
Eis *(n)*   ice
Eisen *(n)*   iron
Eisen-autoklav *(m)*   iron autoclave
  Eisen-katalyse *(f)*   iron catalysis
  Eisen-rohr *(n)*   iron tube
Eis-essig *(m)*   glacial acetic acid
Eiweiss *(n)*   albumin, protein
Eiweiss-körper *(m)*   protein, albuminous substance
elektrisch   electric(al)(ly)
Elektrolyse *(f)*   electrolysis
Elektronen-beugung *(f)*   electron diffraction
Elektronen-formel *(f)*   electronic formula

Elektronen-konfiguration *(f)* electron configuration

Elektronen-stoss *(m)* electron pulse, impact

Elektronen-theorie *(f)* electron theory

Elektronen-verteilung *(f)* electron distribution

Elektronen-zustand *(m)* electronic state

Elementarzelle *(f)* unit cell

elf eleven

elliptisch elliptical

Emissions-banden *(f)* emission bands

Emissions-spektrum *(n)* emission spectrum

Ende *(n)* end

endständig terminal

End-wert *(m)* final value

Energie-differenz *(f)* energy difference

Energie-grösse *(f)* energy parameter

energiereich energy-rich, energetic

Energie-schwelle *(f)* energy threshold, energy barrier

energisch energetic

engl. Ausg. = englische Ausgabe *(f)* English edition

Enolisierung *(f)* enolisation

entfernen to remove, withdraw, separate

    unter Entfernen with removal (of), separation (of)

Entflammbarkeit *(f)* (in)-flammability

Entflammbarkeits-grenze *(f)* limit of flammability

Entflammung *(f)* inflammation (ignition)

entgast degassed

entgegen against, contrary to

entgegengesetzt opposite

enthalten to contain

    enthaltend containing

Entladung *(f)* discharge

Entmischungs-temperatur *(f)* demixing (separation) temperature

entsprechen to correspond to

entsprechend corresponding to

    entspricht corresponds to

entstammen to derive from

entstanden formed

entstehen to originate, result from

    entstehend originating, resulting from

entweichen to escape (fluids)

entwickeln to evolve, liberate, develop

entwicklungshemmend inhibiting development

Entzündbarkeit *(f)* inflammability

entzünden to ignite

Entzündung *(f)* ignition, inflammation

Entzündungs-temperatur *(f)* ignition temperature

21

enzymatisch enzymatic
EPR = Elektronen-paramagne-tische Resonanz (= ESR) *(f)* electron paramagnetic resonance (= ESR)
Erdalkali-metall *(n)* alkaline earth metal
Erdöl *(n)* petroleum, mineral oil
erfassen to collect, gather (data), grasp (idea)
erfolgen to take place
  erfolgt takes place
erforderlich necessary, required
Ergänzung *(f)* supplement, addition (to), complement
Ergänzungs-werk *(n)* Supplementary Series
ergeben to yield, give
  sich ergeben (aus) to result (from)
  die Konfiguration ergibt sich aus the configuration results from
Ergebnis *(n)* result
erhalten to receive, obtain, retain
  sind . . . erhalten worden . . . have been (were) obtained
erhitzen to heat
  beim Erhitzen on heating
erhöhen to increase, raise
Erhöhung *(f)* increase, rise
erkennbar recognizable, perceptible

erkennen to recognize
  ist als . . . erkannt worden has been recognized as
ermitteln to find out, determine
  durch . . . ermittelt determined by . . .
erneut (once) again, once more
Erniedrigung *(f)* lowering
erregend(es Licht) exciting, stimulating (light)
Ersatz *(m)* replacement, substitute, spare
erscheinen to appear
ersetzen to replace, substitute
erst only (temporal sense), not until, firstly
erstarren to solidify
Erstarrungs-diagramm *(n)* solidification (freezing, melting) diagram
Erstarrungs-punkt *(m)* freezing (solidification) point
erste(r) first
erwähnen to mention
erwärmen to warm (up)
erweisen to show, prove
  das sich als . . . erwiesen hat which has proved (shown itself) to be
erzielen to obtain, achieve
Essigsäure *(f)* acetic acid
Essigsäure-anhydrid *(n)* acetic anhydride
Esterifizierung *(f)* esterification

Eutektikum *(n)* eutectic (mixture)
eutektisch eutectic
Existenz *(f)* existence
explodieren to explode
Explosions-grenze *(f)* explosion limit

Explosions-temperatur *(f)* explosion temperature
explosiv explosive
Explosivität *(f)* explosiveness
Extinktion *(f)* extinction, optical density

F

F = Schmelzpunkt(-bereich) *(m)* melting point (range)
Fabrikation *(f)* manufacture
Fall *(m)* case, instance
fällen to precipitate
  gefällt precipitated
falls if, in case of
Fällung *(f)* precipitation
falsch wrong, incorrect
Farbe *(f)* colour
  Farb-reaktion *(f)* colour reaction
Farb-stoff *(m)* dyestuff
farbig colored
farblos colorless
Farbstoff-zwischenprodukt *(n)* dyestuff intermediate
Färbung *(f)* coloration
Faser *(f)* fibre
fast almost
faulend rotting, decaying, putrifying
Fäulnis *(f)* decomposition, putrefaction
fehlen to miss, be lacking

Fehler *(m)* mistake, error
fein fine
Feinstruktur *(f)* fine structure
Feld *(n)* field
Feld-ionisation *(f)* field ionisation
Feld-stärke *(f)* field strength
Fenchel *(m)* fennel
fermentativ fermentational
ferner further, additional(ly)
fest solid
Feststoff *(m)* solid (material)
Fett *(n)* fat
fett fatty, greasy
feucht moist, damp
Feuchtigkeit *(f)* moisture, humidity
Flamme *(f)* flame
Flammen-eigenschaft *(f)* flame property
Flammen-fortpflanzung *(f)* flame propagation
Flammen-spektrum *(n)* flame spectrum

Flammen-temperatur *(f)*
flame temperature
Flamm-geschwindigkeit *(f)*
flame velocity
Flamm-punkt *(m)* flash point
Fleisch-saft *(m)* meat juice(s)
Fliessdruck *(m)* flow pressure
flockig flaky
flüchtig volatile
Fluorescenz-löschung *(f)*
fluorescence quenching
Fluorescenz-spektrum *(n)*
fluorescence spectrum
flüssig (Flüssigkeit *(f)***)** liquid
Flüssigkeit-Dampf-Gleichge-
wicht *(n)* liquid-vapour-
equilibrium
Flüssigkeits-struktur *(f)* liquid structure
Fluss-schlamm *(m)* river mud
Folge *(f)* sequence, series, result
Reaktions-folge *(f)* reaction
sequence
folgen to follow
folgend following
(in) Form (von) (in the) form (of)
Formel *(f)* formula
Formel-register formula index
formulieren to formulate
das als . . . formuliert worden
ist which has been formulated as . . .
ist zu formulieren is to be
formulated (as)
fortgesetzt continued

fortschreiten to proceed, progress
Fortschritt *(m)* progress, development
fraglich questionable
Fragmentierung *(f)* fragmen-
tation
fraktioniert fractioned
frei free
freie Enthalpie free enthalpy
(Gibbs energy)
freisetzen to liberate, set free,
release
freigesetzt liberated
fremd foreign
Fremdgas *(n)* carrier gas
Frequenz *(f)* frequency
Frequenz-abhängigkeit *(f)*
frequency dependence
frisch fresh
Frosch *(m)* frog
Frucht *(f)* fruit
Frucht-wasser *(n)* amniotic
fluid
Frucht-zucker *(m)* fructose
früher earlier, former(ly)
führen (zu) to lead (to), result
(in)
Fuller-erde *(f)* Fuller's earth
fünf five
fünfzehn fifteen
Funken-energie *(f)* spark
energy
Funken-entzündung *(f)* spark
ignition
für for

G

Galle *(f)* bile, gall
(im) Gange (in) process
ganz whole, entire
gären to ferment
Gärung *(f)* fermentation
Gärwirkung *(f)* fermentational effect
Gas *(n)* gas
gasförmig gaseous
Gas-phase *(f)* gas phase
Gas-reaktion *(f)* gas reaction
Gas-zustand *(m)* gaseous state
ge- prefix of past participle, s. verbs without prefix
gealtert aged
geben to give
gibt gives
gegeben given
gebildet formed
Gebiet *(n)* field, area
Gebrauch *(m)* use, practice
gebräuchlich usual
gebunden bonded, bound
geeignet suitable
Gefäss *(n)* vessel, receptacle
Gefäss-wand *(f)* vessel wall
gefolgerte (Existenz) inferred (existence)
Gefrierpunkts-erniedrigung *(f)* freezing point depression
gegen against
Gegengift *(n)* antidote, antitoxin

Gegenmittel *(n)* antidote, remedy
gegenseitig mutual
Gegenstrom *(m)* countercurrent
Gegenstrom-verteilung *(f)* countercurrent distribution
Gegenwart *(f)* present (time), presence
gegoren fermented
Gehalt *(m)* content
gekörnt granulated
gekreuzt crossed
gekühlt cooled
geladen loaded, charged
gelatinös gelatinous
gelb(lich) yellow(ish)
gelbbraun yellow-brown
gelbgrün yellow-green
gelblich weiss yellowish white
gelborangefarben yellow-orange coloured
gelegen placed, put
gelegentlich occasional(ly), sometimes
gelinde mild(ly), soft(ly)
gelöst dissolved
gemeinsam (in) common, joint
Gemenge *(n)* mixture
Gemisch *(n)* mixture
genannt named
genau exact(ly)
gepuffert buffered

Gerbstoff *(m)* tanning agent
gereinigt cleaned
gering slight, small
geringer lesser, minor
geröstet roasted, smelted
Geruch *(m)* odour
Gerüst *(n)* frame (work), skeleton
Gesamt-menge *(f)* total quantity
gesättigt saturated
geschlossen closed, concluded
Geschmack *(m)* flavour, taste
geschmolzen melted, molten
Geschwindigkeit *(f)* velocity, rate
Geschwindigkeits-konstante *(f)* rate constant
gesichert verified, secured
gestreut scattered, spread
getränkt soaked, impregnated
getrennt separate(ly), separated
getrocknet dried
Gewebe *(n)* tissue, texture
gewesen been
  ist gewesen has been
  sind gewesen have been
Gew.-% = Gewichts-prozent *(n)* percent by weight
Gewicht *(n)* weight
Gewinnung *(f)* extraction, isolation
gewiss certain(ly)
gewöhnlich usual(ly)
gewogen weighed

geworden (has, have) been (with past participle)
gibt gives
Gift *(n)* poison, toxin, venom
giftig poisonous, toxic
Gift-wirkung *(f)* toxic effect
Gitter *(n)* lattice
Gitter-konstante *(f)* lattice constant
Glas *(n)* glass
glasartig glassy, vitreous
Glas-rohr *(n)* glass tube, tubing
(in) glatter (Weise) smoothly
gleich same, equal
gleichfalls equally, likewise
Gleichgewicht *(n)* equilibrium
Gleichgewichts-abstand *(m)* equilibrium distance
Gleichgewichts-einstellung *(f)* equilibration
Gleichgewichts-konstante *(f)* equilibrium constant
gleichmässig even(ly)
Gleichmässigkeit *(f)* uniformity, evenness
gleichmolekular equimolecular
Gleichstrom *(m)* direct current
Gleichung *(f)* equation
gleichzeitig simultaneous(ly)
Glimmlicht-entladung *(f)* glow discharge
glühend glowing (hot)
Glühlampe *(f)* incandescent lamp, electric bulb

Glühlampen-licht *(n)* electric light, incandescent light
Gold *(n)* gold
goldbraun gold brown
grad = Grad *(m)* degree
granuliert granulated
grau grey
  graugrün grey-green
gravimetrisch gravimetric
Grenz-fläche *(f)* interface, boundary surface
Grenzflächen-spannung *(f)* interfacial tension
Grenz-konzentration *(f)* limiting concentration
Grenz-temperatur *(f)* limiting temperature
Grenz-wert *(m)* limiting value, limit
Grenz-zusammensetzung *(f)* limiting composition
gross large, great
  grösser larger, greater

grösste(r) largest, greatest
grün green
  grünblau blue-green
  grünbraun green-brown
  grüngelb yellow-green
  grünschwarz greenish black
Grund *(m)* ground, reason, basis
  auf Grund because of, on account of
(sich) gründen (auf) to base on
Grundschwingungs-bande *(f)* fundamental vibration(al) band
Grundschwingungs-frequenz *(f)* fundamental vibration(al) frequency
Grund-zustand *(m)* ground state
Grünspan *(m)* verdigris
Gruppe *(f)* group
Güte *(f)* quality

H = Hauptwerk des Beilstein-Handbuchs Beilstein basic series
h = Stunde *(f)* hour
Habilitations-schrift *(f)* habilitation treatise (qualification for higher office, esp. in German universities)
halb half

Halbachse *(f)* half-axis, half-axle
Halbstufen-potential *(n)* half-wave potential
Halbwertszeit *(f)* half-life
Hälfte *(f)* half, moiety
Halogenid *(n)* halide
Halogenierung *(f)* halogenation

haltbar durable, stable
Handels-wert *(m)* commercial value
Harn *(m)* urine
Harnsäure *(f)* uric acid
Harnstoff *(m)* urea
Harz *(n)* resin, gum
harzig resinous
Hauptbestandteil *(m)* main component
Hauptprodukt *(n)* main product
hauptsächlich main(ly), principal(ly)
Hauptwerk *(n)* Basic Series (of Beilstein)
Haut-verätzung *(f)* skin burns (chemical)
Hefe *(f)* yeast
heftig violent(ly)
heiss hot
hell light
   hellblau light blue
   hellbraun light brown
   hellgelb light yellow
   hellgrün light green
   hellrot light red
hemmen to inhibit, retard
heraus out
Herkunft *(f)* origin
herstellen to prepare, manufacture
   analog hergestellt analogously prepared
Herstellung *(f)* preparation, manufacture

Herstellungs-weise *(f)* manner of preparation
hervorgehen (aus) to originate (from), result (from)
hervorrufen to cause, give rise (to), produce
   ruft . . . hervor gives rise (to), causes, produces
Herz *(n)* heart
hierfür for it (this)
hiermit with it (this), herewith
Hilfe *(f)* aid, help
   mit Hilfe von with the aid of, by means of
Hinblick *(m)* view, regard
   im Hinblick auf in view of, with regard to
hindern to prevent, hinder, impede
hingegen on the other hand, on the contrary, however
Hinweis *(m)* indication, hint, reference
hinzufügen to add
Hitze *(f)* heat
hoch, hohe(r, s) high
   höher higher
   höher siedend higher-boiling
   höchst highest
   höchstens at (the) most
Hochdruck *(m)* high pressure
hochfrequent high-frequency
Hochfrequenz *(f)* high frequency
hochsiedend high-boiling
Hochvakuum *(n)* high vacuum

Holz-essig *(m)* pyroligneous acid, wood vinegar
Holz-kohle *(f)* wood charcoal
homogen homogeneous(ly)
homöopolar homopolar
Hühner-ei *(n)* hen's egg
Hund *(m)* dog
hundert hundred
Hydratation *(f)* hydration
Hydratisierung *(f)* hydration
hydrieren to hydrogenate

Hydrierung *(f)* hydrogenation
Hydrierungs-wärme *(f)* heat of hydrogenation
Hydrierungs-temperatur *(f)* hydrogenation temperature
Hydrochinon *(n)* hydroquinone
Hydrolyse *(f)* hydrolysis
hygroskopisch hygroscopic
Hz = **Hertz** $(= s^{-1})$ hertz, cycles per second $(= s^{-1})$

I

identisch identical
Identität *(f)* identity
im in the
immer always
impfen to inocculate, vaccinate, seed
imprägnieren to impregnate
in in, into
indizieren indicate
induziert induced
infolge as a result of, because of
Inhalt *(m)* content(s), capacity (of a vessel)
initiiert initiated
inner internal
innig intimate
insbesondere especially, particularly
insgesamt altogether

Intensität *(f)* intensity
Ionen-beweglichkeit *(f)* ion mobility
Ionen-produkt *(n)* ionic product
Ionen-stärke *(f)* ionic strength
Ionisierungs-potential *(n)* ionization potential
Ionisierungs-querschnitt *(m)* ionization cross section
irritativ irritant
Irrtum *(m)* error
irrtümlich erroneously
isentrop isentropic
isocyclisch isocyclic
Isolierung *(f)* isolation, insulation
isotherm isothermal
isotrop isotropic
ist is

J

Jahr *(n)* year
jede(r) each, every
jedoch however
je nach according to
jeweils in each case, each time

Jod *(n)* iodine
jodhaltig containing iodine
Jodierung *(f)* iodation, iodination

K

Kaffee *(m)* coffee
Kalilauge *(f)* potassium hydroxide solution, caustic potash
Kalium *(n)* potassium
Kalk *(m)* lime, limestone, chalk
Kalk-milch *(f)* milk of lime (aqueous slurry of calcium hydroxide)
kalt cold
Kälte *(f)* cold(ness)
Kälte-mischung *(f)* freezing mixture
Kamille *(f)* camomile
Kaninchen *(n)* rabbit
kann can, is able
Kapazität *(f)* capacity
Kapillare *(f)* capillary
Karminrot *(n)* carmine red, crimson lake
Kartoffel *(f)* potato
Käse *(m)* cheese

Katalysator *(m)* catalyst
katalysieren to catalyse
katalytisch catalytic
Kathoden-strahl *(m)* cathode ray
Kationen-austauscher *(m)* cation exchanger
Katze *(f)* cat
kaukasisch caucasian
Kautschuk *(m)* caoutchouc, rubber (gummi elasticum)
Kautschuk-industrie *(f)* caoutchouc, rubber industry
kein(e) no, not . . . any, none
Kennzeichen *(n)* characteristic, distinguishing feature, label
Kern *(m)* nucleus, kernel
Kern-quadrupol-kopplungs-konstante *(f)* nuclear quadrupole coupling constant
Kern-Spin-Relaxations-zeit *(f)* nuclear spin relaxation time

Kessel *(m)* boiler, kettle, vessel

Kette *(f)* chain

Kieselgel *(n)* silicagel

Kieselgur *(m)* diatomaceous earth, kieselguhr

Kieselsäure *(f)* silicic acid

kinematisch kinematic

Kinetik *(f)* kinetics

kinetische Energie *(f)* kinetic energy

klar clear

klein small

kleiner smaller

Knall-quecksilber *(n)* fulminate of mercury, mercuric fulminate

Knallsäure *(f)* fulminic acid

Knick-schwingung *(f)* bending vibration

koagulierend coagulating

kochen to boil

Kochsalz *(n)* common salt, sodium chloride

Kohle *(f)* coal, charcoal, carbon

Kohle-Lichtbogen *(m)* carbon arc

Kohlen-dioxid *(n)* carbon dioxide

Kohlen-monoxid *(n)* carbon monoxide

Kohlensäure *(f)* carbon dioxide, carbonic acid

Kohlenstoff *(m)* carbon

Kohlen-suboxid *(n)* carbon suboxide

Kohlen-wasserstoff *(m)* hydrocarbon

Koks *(m)* coke

kommt ... zu comes (up) to, in addition (to)

Komplexbildungs-tendenz *(f)* complex-forming tendency

Komponente *(f)* component

Kompressibilität *(f)* compressibility

komprimiert compressed

Kondensations-mittel *(n)* means of condensing

kondensiert condensed

konduktometrisch conductometric

Konfigurations-bestimmung *(f)* configurational determination

Konfigurations-zuordnung *(f)* configurational assignment

konjugiert conjugated

konkurrierende Reaktion *(f)* competitive reaction

können can, to be able

Konservierungs-mittel *(n)* preservative

Konstante *(f)* constant

Kontakt-winkel *(m)* angle of contact

Kontakt-zeit *(f)* contact time

konz. = konzentriert concentrated

Konzentration *(f)* concentration

Kopplung *(f)* coupling
Kopplungs-konstante *(f)*
  coupling constant
korallenartig coral like
Körper *(m)* body, substance
korr. = korrigiert corr. = corrected
Kost *(f)* food, diet
Kp = Siedepunkt(-bereich) *(m)*
  boiling point (range)
Kraft *(f)* force, power, strength
Kraft-konstante *(f)* force constant
kranzförmig coronoid,
  wreath-shaped
kreuzen to cross
Kristall *(m)* crystal
Kristall-achse *(f)* crystal axis
kristallin crystalline
Kristall-modifikation *(f)*
  crystal modification
Kristall-morphologie *(f)*
  crystal morphology
Kristall-optik *(f)* crystal optics
Kristall-struktur *(f)* crystal
  structure
Kristallstruktur-analyse *(f)*
  crystal structure analysis

Kristall-wachstum *(n)* crystal
  growth
Kristall-wasser *(n)* water of
  crystallization
kritisch critical
Kryoskopie *(f)* cryoscopy
kryoskopisch cryoscopic
Krystall s. Kristall
kubisch cubic
kühl cool
kühlen to cool
Kühler *(m)* condenser
Kühlhaus *(n)* cold storage
  house
Kühlung *(f)* cooling
Kümmel *(m)* caraway (seed)
kumuliert (ac)cumulated
Kunstharz *(n)* synthetic, artifical resin
künstlich synthetic, artificial
Küpe *(f)* vat (liquor, dye)
Kupfer *(n)* copper
Kupfer-block *(m)* copper
  block
kurz short
Kurve *(f)* curve

L

l = (1) **Liter** *(m)* litre
(2) **Rohr-länge** *(f)* in dm
length of tube (polarimetry)
in dm
Lack *(m)* laquer, varnish, oil-
based paint
Lackmus-papier *(n)* litmus
paper
laden to charge (electrically)
Ladung *(f)* charge
Lähmung *(f)* lameness, para-
lysis
Lage *(f)* position
lang long
langsam slow(ly)
Laub-holz *(n)* deciduous
wood
laufend running, continuous-
(ly), current (year etc.)
Lauge alkaline solution
l. c. loc. cit. = *loco citato*
Lebens-dauer *(f)* lifetime, dur-
ability
Lebensmittel-chemie *(f)* food
chemistry
Leber *(f)* liver
Legierung *(f)* alloy
leicht light, easy, easily
leicht löslich easily soluble
Leicht-metall *(n)* light metal
Leicht-öl *(n)* light oil
leiten to conduct (electricity),
lead, guide, direct, manage

Leitfähigkeit *(f)* conductivity
Leitvermögen *(n)* conduction,
conductivity
letal lethal, fatal
letzte last
letztere the latter
leuchten to (give) light, shine,
glow
leuchtend luminous, bright,
shining
Leucht-gas *(n)* (lighting) gas,
coal gas
Licht *(n)* light
Licht-ausbeute *(f)* light yield
Licht-ausschluss *(m)* exclusion of light
Licht-bogen *(m)* (electric) arc
Licht-emission *(f)* light emission
lichtinduziert (Reaktion) light
induced (reaction)
Licht-intensität *(f)* light intensity
Licht-streuung *(f)* light scattering
liefern to deliver, provide, give
Linie *(f)* line
Linien-breite *(f)* line width
links left
linksdrehend levorotatory
Literatur-quelle *(f)* literature
source, reference
locker loose

Löschung *(f)* quenching, extinguishing, discharge
lösen to solve, dissolve
löslich soluble
Löslichkeit *(f)* solubility
Löslichkeits-diagramm *(n)* solubility diagram
Lösungs-enthalpie *(f)* enthalpy of solution
Lösungs-gleichgewicht *(n)* solution equilibrium
Lösungs-mittel *(n)* solvent

Lösungs-temperatur *(f)* solution temperature
Lösungs-vermögen *(n)* dissolving power
Lösungs-wärme *(f)* heat of solution
Luft *(f)* air
Luft-strom *(m)* air stream, air current
Luft-zutritt *(m)* air access
Luminescenz *(f)* luminescence
Lunge *(f)* lung(s)

m = (1) **Meter** *(n)* meter
(2) **Molarität einer Lösung** *(f)* molarity of solution
Magen *(m)* stomach
magnetisch magnetic
Magneto-rotation *(f)* magnet rotation (Faraday effect)
Maische *(f)* mash
makromolekular macromolecular
Malonsäure *(f)* malonic acid
Malz-auszug *(m)* malt extract
Masse *(f)* mass, bulk
Massen-spektrum *(n)* mass spectrum
Massen-spektrometrie *(f)* mass spectrometry
massen-spektrometrisch mass spectrometric(ally)

mässig moderate(ly)
Massstab *(m)* scale
Me. = **Methanol** *(n)* methanol
Mechanismus *(m)* mechanism
Meerschweinchen *(n)* guinea pig
mehr more
mehrere several
mehrfach multiple, manifold
Mehrheit *(f)* majority
mehrkernig polynuclear
mehrmals (mehrmalig) several times
mehrmonatig for several months
Mehrstoff-system *(n)* multicomponent system
mehrstündig for several hours
mehrtägig for several days

mehrwöchig for several weeks
meiste most
meist(ens) most(ly)
Melasse-sirup *(m)* molasses
Menge *(f)* amount, quantity
Mengen-verhältnis *(n)* ratio, proportion
Mensch *(m)* man (collectively), human (-being)
menschlich human
Merkmal *(n)* characteristic, feature
Mesoweinsäure *(f)* meso tartaric acid
messen to measure
Messung *(f)* measurement
metallisch metallic
Metall-oberfläche *(f)* metal surface
Methode *(f)* method
mikrochemisch microchemical
Mikrowellen-Spektrum *(n)* microwave spectrum
Milch *(f)* milk
Milchsäure *(f)* lactic acid
Milz *(f)* spleen
mindestens at least
Mineral-säure *(f)* mineral acid
Mischbarkeit *(f)* miscibility
mischen to mix
  gemischt mixed
  mischbar miscible
Mischkristall *(m)* mixed crystal
Mischung *(f)* mixture
Mischungs-diagramm *(n)* mis-cibility diagram, mixture curve
Mischungs-enthalpie *(f)* enthalpy of mixing
Mischungs-temperatur *(f)* mixing temperature
Mischungs-verhältnis *(n)* mixture ratio
Mischungs-volumen *(n)* mixing volume
Mischungs-vorgang *(m)* process of mixing
mit with
Mitteilung *(f)* communication
Mittel *(n)* mean
Mitteldruck *(m)* medium pressure
mittels by means of
mittelständig in a middle (central) position
mittlere average, mean
möglich(erweise) possible (possibly)
möglichst ... (z. B. **viel**) at most, as ... (e.g. much) as possible
molar molar
Molekül-gestalt *(f)* molecular shape
Molekül-schwingung *(f)* molecular vibration
Mol-polarisation *(f)* molar polarisation
Mol-verhältnis *(n)* molar ratio
Mol-volumen *(n)* molar volume

momentan momentary, at the moment

Monat *(m)* month

monoklin monoclinic

monomolekular unimolecular

Muskel *(m)* muscle

müssen must
  muss must

Mutter-lauge *(f)* mother liquor

N

n = (1) bei Dimensionen von Elementarzellen: **Anzahl der Formeleinheiten pro Elementarzelle** number of formula units in the unit cell
(2) **Normalität einer Lösung** normality of solution
(3) **nano** (= 10^{-9}) nano (= 10^{-9})
(4) **Brechungsindex** refractive index

nach after, according to

nacheinander successively

nachfolgend subsequent, following

nachleuchten to glow (after an event)

nachstehend following

Nachtrag *(m)* addendum

Nachweis *(m)* evidence, detection, proof

nachweisbar demonstrable, detectable

nachweisen to detect, prove
  ist ... nachgewiesen worden ... has been shown, demonstrated, proven

Nadel *(f)* needle, pin

Nadel-holz *(n)* coniferous wood

nahe near, neighbouring
  näher nearer
  nahezu almost, approximately

Nähe *(f)* neighbourhood, vicinity, proximity

Nahrungs-mittel *(n)* food (stuff)

nämlich that is, i.e., in particular

Natrium *(n)* sodium

Natronlauge *(f)* sodium hydroxide solution, caustic soda

neben beside, as well as

Nebenprodukt *(n)* side-product, by-product

nebenstehend adjoining

Nekrose *(f)* necrosis

nekrotisierend necrotizing

Netz-ebenen-abstand *(m)* (lattice) spacing

neun nine

Neutralmolekül *(n)* neutral molecule

Neutronen-Beugung *(f)* neutron diffraction
nicht not, non-
Niederfrequenz *(f)* low frequency
Niederschlag *(m)* precipitate, deposit, condensation
niedrig low
　niedriger lower
nie(-mals) never
Niere *(f)* kidney
Nitrierung *(f)* nitration
Nitrosierung *(f)* nitrosation

noch still, yet
nochmalig repeated
Normalbedingung *(f)* standard condition
Normaldruck *(m)* standard (normal) pressure
notwendig necessary (necessarily)
Nullpunkt-energie *(f)* zero point energy
nunmehr now
nur only

○

oben above, overhead, on top, on the surface
ober(e) upper
Oberfläche *(f)* surface
Oberflächen-aktivität *(f)* surface activity
Oberflächen-potential *(n)* surface potential
Oberflächen-spannung *(f)* surface tension
oberhalb above
obig above, foregoing (text etc.)
oder or
offen open
offenbar evident(ly), obvious-(ly), clear(ly), apparent(ly)
offensichtlich see offenbar

ohne without
Öl *(n)* oil
ölig oily
Ölsäure *(f)* oleic acid
Önanthsäure *(f)* heptanoic (enanthic) acid
opt.-akt. = **optisch aktiv** optically active
opt.-inakt. = **optisch inaktiv** optically inactive
optisch optical(ly)
orangefarben orange coloured
orange orange
orangerot orange-red
Ordnung *(f)* order(ing), arrangement
Organ *(n)* organ (body etc.), medium (of publication etc.)

Orientierung *(f)* orientation
Orientierungs-polarisation *(f)* orientation(al) polarization
orthorhombisch orthorhombic
Östradiol *(n)* (o)estradiol
Östron *(n)* (o)estrone

Oszillator *(m)* oscillator
Oszillator-stärke *(f)* oscillator strength
Oxalsäure *(f)* oxalic acid
ozonisiert ozonized

PAe. = **Petroläther** *(m)* petroleum ether
Paraffin *(n)* paraffin wax, paraffin (C_nH_{2n+2})
paraffiniert coated with paraffin wax
paramagnetisch paramagnetic
paraständig in (the) para position
Partialdruck *(m)* partial pressure
partiell partial(ly)
periodisch periodic
Petrol-äther *(m)* petroleum ether
Pfefferminz-öl *(n)* peppermint oil
Pflanze *(f)* plant
pflanzlich(e Herkunft) (of) vegetable (origin)
pharmazeutisch pharmaceutic(al)
Phasen-diagramm *(n)* phase diagram
Phasen-gleichgewicht *(n)* phase equilibrium

Phasen-grenze *(f)* phase boundary
Phasen-umwandlung *(f)* phase transformation
Phosphor *(m)* phosphorus
Phosphorescenz *(f)* phosphorescence
photochemisch photochemical
photoelektrisch photoelectric(al)
Photolyse *(f)* photolysis
photolytisch photolytic
Photomagnetismus *(m)* photomagnetism
Photoreaktion *(f)* photo reaction
physikalisch physical
physiologisch physiological
piezoelektrisch piezoelectric
Pikrinsäure *(f)* picric acid
Pilz *(m)* fungus, agaric, mushroom
Platin-elektrode *(f)* platinum electrode
Platin-schale *(f)* platinum dish

Polarisations-grad *(m)* degree of polarization
Polarisierbarkeit *(f)* polarizability
Polarisierbarkeits-ellipsoid *(n)* polarizability ellipsoid
polarisiert polarized
Polarographie *(f)* polarography
polykristallin polycrystalline
Porzellan-rohr *(n)* porcellan tube, tubing
Potential-differenz *(f)* potential difference
Potential-schwelle *(f)* potential barrier
Potential-verlauf *(m)* potential curve
potentiometrisch potentiometric
Pottasche *(f)* potash, potassium carbonate
Präparat *(n)* compound, preparation

präparativ preparative
primär primary
Primärstadium *(n)* primary stage
Produkt *(n)* product
Produkt-ausbeute *(f)* product yield
Produktions-ausbeute *(f)* production yield, output
Protonen-affinität *(f)* proton affinity
protoniert protonated
Protonierungs-gleichgewicht *(n)* protonation equilibrium
Prüfung *(f)* test(ing), examination
Puffer *(m)* buffer
puffern to buffer
Pulver *(n)* powder
Punkt *(m)* point
Py. = **Pyridin** *(n)* pyridine
pyrogen pyrogenic
Pyrolyse *(f)* pyrolysis

Q

Quadrupel-punkt *(m)* quadruple point
Quanten-ausbeute *(f)* quantum yield
quantitativ quantitative
qua(r)ternär quaternary
Quarz *(m)* quartz
Quarz-rohr *(n)* quartz tube, tubing
Quarz-sand *(m)* quartz sand
Quecksilber *(n)* mercury
Quelle *(f)* source
Quellung *(f)* swelling
Querschnitt *(m)* cross-section
quinär quinary

R

racemisieren to racemize
Radikal *(n)* radical
Rand-winkel *(m)* contact angle, edge angle
ranzig rancid
rasch rapid(ly)
Ratte *(f)* rat
rauchen to fume, smoke
  rauchend fuming, smoking
Raum-gruppe *(f)* space group
Raum-temperatur *(f)* room temperature
Rayleigh-Streuung *(f)* Rayleigh-scattering
Reagenz *(n)* reagent
reaktionsfördernd favouring, promoting reaction
Reaktions-gefäss *(n)* reaction vessel
Reaktions-gemisch *(n)* reaction mixture
Reaktions-geschwindigkeit *(f)* reaction rate
Reaktions-lösung *(f)* reaction solution
Reaktions-partner *(m)* reactant
Reaktions-produkt *(n)* reaction produkt
Reaktions-system *(n)* reaction system
Reaktions-zone *(f)* reaction zone

Reaktivität *(f)* reactivity
Reaktor *(m)* reactor
Reaktor-beschaffenheit *(f)* reactor constitution (nature of materials used)
Reaktor-wand *(f)* reactor wall
rechts right
rechtsdrehend dextrorotatory
reflektieren to reflect
Reflexions-Bande *(f)* reflexion band
refractometrisch refractometric
Reihe *(f)* series, row, sequence
Reihenfolge *(f)* order, sequence
rein pure, clean
reinblau pure blue
Reindarstellung *(f)* preparation in a pure state
Reingewinnung *(f)* preparation (isolation) in a pure state
Reinheit *(f)* purity
Reinheits-prüfung *(f)* test of purity
Reinigung *(f)* purification, cleaning
Reis *(m)* rice
Reis-kleie *(f)* rice bran
Reizung *(f)* stimulation, irritation
Reizungs-stadium *(n)* stage, degree of stimulation, irritation

relativ relative
Relaxations-zeit *(f)* relaxation time
Resonanz *(f)* resonance
Resonanz-Raman-Effekt *(m)* resonance Raman effect
resorptiv resorptive
Rest *(m)* residue, remains, rest
restlich residual, remaining
Retorte *(f)* retort
richtig correct, right
Richtung *(f)* direction, orientation
riechen to smell
Rind *(n)* ox, cow, steer
Rinde *(f)* bark, rind, crust
Ring *(m)* ring, cycle
Rohphenol *(n)* crude phenol
Rohprodukt *(n)* crude, raw product
Rohr *(n)* tube, tubing
Rohr-länge *(f)* length of tube
Rohr-zucker *(m)* cane sugar (sucrose)
Röntgen-Diagramm *(n)* X-ray pattern
Röntgen-Luminescenzspektrum *(n)* X-ray luminescence spectrum
röntgenographisch radiographical (by means of X-rays)
Röntgen-Strahlen *(m)* X-rays
rosarot pink

Rost *(m)* rust
rostfrei rust-proof, stainless
rot red
rötlich reddish
rötlichgelb reddish yellow
Rotations-konstante *(f)* rotational constant
Rotations-linie *(f)* rotational line
Rotations-sprung(übergang) *(m)* rotational transition
Rotations-Raman-Spektrum *(n)* rotational Raman spectrum
Rotations-struktur *(f)* rotational structure
rotierend rotating
Rötung *(f)* reddening
Rücken-mark *(n)* spinal marrow, cord
Rückfluss *(m)* reflux
Rückgewinnung *(f)* recovery
Rückstand *(m)* residue
rückwärts back(wards)
ruft . . . hervor gives rise to, results in, produces
ruhend (in the) quiescent (condition), (in the) stationary (condition)
rühren to stir
  unter Rühren with stirring
Rührwerk *(n)* stirrer
russend smoky, smoking, sooty

S

S. = **Seite** *(f)* page
s = **Sekunde** *(f)* second
s. = **siehe** see
s. a. (siehe auch) see also
Sach-register *(n)* subject index (compound name index)
Saft *(m)* juice, sap, liquor
Salpetersäure *(f)* nitric acid
Salz *(n)* salt
salzsauer containing hydrochloric acid
Salzsäure *(f)* hydrochloric acid
Samen *(m)* seed, semen
sättigen to saturate
　gesättigt saturated
Sättigung *(f)* saturation
Sättigungs-druck *(m)* saturation pressure
sauer acidic, sour
Sauerstoff *(m)* oxygen
Sauerstoff-entwicklung *(f)* oxygen generation
Sauerstoff-verbrauch *(m)* oxygen consumption
sauer werden to turn (become) acid
Säure *(f)* acid
schädigen to injure, harm, damage
Schaf *(n)* sheep
Schall *(m)* sound

Schall-absorption *(f)* sound absorption
Schall-dispersion *(f)* sound dispersion
Schall-frequenz *(f)* sound frequency
Schall-geschwindigkeit *(f)* sound velocity
Schall-messung *(f)* sound measurement
Schall-relaxation *(f)* sound relaxation
Schaum *(m)* foam, froth
schäumen to foam, froth, fizz (drinks), sparkle (wines)
scheinbar seeming(ly), apparent(ly)
Schicht *(f)* layer, film, stratum, charge (of furnace)
Schicht-dicke *(f)* layer, film thickness
Schiefer *(m)* shale, slate
Schiefer-öl *(n)* shale oil
Schildkröte *(f)* tortoise, turtle
Schimmel *(m)* mould, mildew
Schimmel-pilz *(m)* mould fungus
schlecht bad(ly), poor(ly) (yield etc.)
Schleimsäure *(f)* mucic acid, galactaric acid

schliessen to close, conclude
  geschlossen closed, concluded
schliesslich finally, ultimately
Schluss *(m)* finish, end, conclusion
Schmelz-diagramm *(n)* melting diagram
Schmelze *(f)* melt
schmelzen to melt
  schmelzend melting
  geschmolzen fused, molten, melted
Schmelz-enthalpie *(f)* enthalpy of fusion
Schmelz-punkt *(m)* melting point
Schmelz-wärme *(f)* heat of fusion
Schmiermittel *(n)* lubricant
schnell fast, quick(ly)
schon already
Schuppe *(f)* scale, flake
schütteln to shake, agitate
  beim Schütteln on shaking
schwach weak(ly)
schwanken to vary, fluctuate
Schwankungs-breite *(f)* range of variation, fluctuation
schwarzblau blue-black
schwarzgrün greenish-black
schwarzrot reddish-black
schwarzviolett violet-black
Schwefel *(m)* sulphur
Schwefelsäure *(f)* sulphuric acid

Schwefel-farbstoff *(m)* sulphur dye
Schwefel-kohlenstoff *(m)* carbon disulfide
schwefelsäurehaltig containing sulphuric acid
Schwefel-wasserstoff *(m)* hydrogen sulfide
schwef(e)lige Säure *(f)* sulphurous acid
Schweiss *(m)* sweat
schwer heavy, difficult
  schwer löslich difficultly soluble
Schwere-feld *(n)* gravitation-(al) field
Schwermetall *(n)* heavy metal
Schweröl *(n)* heavy oil
Schwingung *(f)* vibration
Schwingungs-bande *(f)* vibrational band
Schwingungs-relaxations-zeit *(f)* vibrational relaxation time
sechs six
sechs-gliedrig six-membered
sechsseitig six-sided, hexagonal
sechzig sixty
sehr very, very much
Seiden-fibroin *(m)* fibroin
Seife *(f)* soap
Seifen-lösung *(f)* soap solution
sein (1) its, his (2) to be
Seite *(f)* page

Seiten-kette *(f)* sidechain
sekundär secondary
Sekunde *(f)* second
selb(e) same, identical
selbst itself, himself
selbständig independent(ly), self-contained
Selbstdiffusions-koeffizient *(m)* self-diffusion coefficient
Selbstentzündung *(f)* self ignition
Selbstentzündungs-temperatur *(f)* self ignition point, spontaneous ignition temperature
Selbstkondensation *(f)* self condensation, autocondensation
selektiv selective
selten seldom, rare(ly)
setzen to put, place, set, plant
  gesetzt put, placed, set, planted
sichern to secure, safeguard
  gesichert secured, safeguarded, ensured, verified
sichtbar visible, conspicuous
sieben seven
sieden to boil
  siedend boiling
  zum Sieden (bringen) (bring) to the boil
Siedehitze *(f)* boiling heat
Siedepunkt *(m)* boiling point
Siedetemperatur *(f)* boiling temperature
siehe see

Silber *(n)* silver
Silicium *(n)* silicon
sind are (have, as auxiliary verb)
sinken to sink, decrease, subside
sintern to sinter
snF = siehe nebenstehende Formel see adjacent formula
so so, thus
  so dass so that
  so viel so much, many
s. o. = siehe oben see above
(in) sofern as far as, in as much as
sofort immediately, at once
sog. = sogenannt so-called
Solubilisierung *(f)* solubilization
Solvatation *(f)* solva(ta)tion
Solvolyse *(f)* solvolysis
Sonderband *(m)* special volume
Sonderheft (Sonderh.) *(n)* special part, number (of publication)
sondern but, rather
  (nicht . . . sondern . . .) (not . . . but . . .)
Sonnen-licht *(n)* sunlight
Sonoluminescenz *(f)* sonoluminescence
sonst otherwise, else, besides
sorgfältig careful(ly)
Sorption *(f)* sorption
Sorptions-isotherme *(f)* sorp-

tion isotherm
sowie as well as, and
spalten to split, cleave, fissure, divide
 gespalten split, cloven
Spaltung *(f)* split, cleavage, scission
Spaltpilz *(m)* fission fungus
Spannung *(f)* tension, voltage
spät(er) late(r)
Speichel *(m)* saliva
spektrophotometrisch spectrophotometric
spektroskopisch spectroscopic
spezifisch specific
Spiegel-bild *(n)* mirror image
Spiegel-wirkung *(f)* mirror effect
Spinat *(m)* spinach
Spiritus *(m)* spirit(s), rectified spirits
Spl. = Supplement *(n)* supplement
Spreitungs-druck *(m)* spreading pressure
Sprengstoff *(m)* explosive
Spur *(f)* trace
Stäbchen *(n)* small rod
stabil stable
Stabilitäts-konstante *(f)* stability constant
Stahl *(m)* steel
Standard-Gibbs-Lösungsenergie *(f)* standard Gibb's energy of solution
ständig permanent, constant, fixed

stark strong, powerful, thick (vessel walls, sheet metal etc.)
Stärke *(f)* (1) strength, (2) starch
Stärke-lösung *(f)* starch solution
Stärke-zucker *(m)* (D-)Glucose, starch sugar
starr rigid
stationär stationary
statisch static
statistisch statistic(al)
statt instead of
stattfinden to take place
 findet ... statt takes place
Staub *(m)* dust
...-stdg. for ... hours
 z. B. 4-stündig e. g. for 4 hours, over 4 hours
stehen lassen to leave (standing) unchanged
steigen to climb, rise, increase
Steigerung *(f)* increase, rise, enhancement
Steinkohlen-teer *(m)* coal tar
Stelle *(f)* place, position
 an Stelle von instead of
Stellen-bezeichnung *(f)* positional designation
Stellung *(f)* position, attitude, disposition
Stengel *(m)* stalk, stem
stereochemisch stereochemical
stereospezifisch stereospecific
stetig, stets invariable(ly) con-

stant(ly), continual(ly), always

Stickstoff *(m)* nitrogen

Stickstoff-wasserstoff-säure *(f)* hydrazoic acid

still still, stationary, quiet

stöchiometrisch stoichiometric

Stoff *(m)* substance, material, (subject) matter

Stoffwechsel *(m)* metabolism

Stöpsel-glas *(n)* stoppered tube

Stoss *(m)* collision, impact, (im)pulse

Stoss-ausbeute *(f)* collision yield

Stoss-querschnitt *(m)* collision cross-section

Stosswelle *(f)* shock wave

Strahl(en) *(m)* ray(s), beam(s), jet(s)

strahlig radiated, radiant, -jet (jetted)

Strahlung *(f)* radiation

Streckschwingung *(f)* stretching vibration

streng strict, rigorous, severe

streuen to scatter, spread

Streulicht *(n)* scattered light

Streuquerschnitt *(m)* scattering cross-section

Streuung *(f)* scattering

Strom *(m)* current, stream (elec. or water)

  Strom-dichte *(f)* current density

Strom-spannungs-kurve *(f)* current-potential (voltage) curve

Strom-stärke *(f)* current strength

strömen to flow, stream

  strömend flowing, streaming

Strömung *(f)* flow, stream-(ing), current (water etc.), flux

Strömungs-Doppelbrechung *(f)* streaming birefringence

Struktur *(f)* structure

Stufe *(f)* stage, step, degree

  Reaktions-stufe *(f)* reaction stage

Stunde *(f)* hour

s. u. = **siehe unten** see below

subcutan subcutaneous

Sublimations-enthalpie *(f)* enthalpy of sublimation

Sublimations-punkt *(m)* sublimation point

sublimierbar sublimable

Substanz *(f)* substance

substituiert substituted

Sulfurierung *(f)* sulphurization

Summen-formel *(f)* empirical (stoichiometric) formula

Susceptibilität *(f)* susceptibility

süss sweet

systematisch systematically

Syst.-Nr. = **System-Nummer** *(f)* system number

T

Tabak *(m)* tobacco
Tafel *(f)* plate
Täfelchen *(n)* platelet
Tag *(m)* day
  ... **tägig** for ... days
  (z. B. **dreitägig** e. g. for 3 days)
tagelang for days
täglich daily
Tages-licht *(n)* daylight
Tätigkeit *(f)* activity, functioning, operation, occupation
technisch technical
Teer *(m)* tar
teerig tarry
Teer-verwertung *(f)* tar utilization
Teil *(m)* part, portion, piece
Teilchen *(n)* particle(s)
teilweise partly, partial(ly)
Temperatur-abhängigkeit *(f)* temperature dependence
Temperatur-änderung *(f)* temperature change
Temperatur-bereich *(m)* temperature range
ternär ternary
Terpentin-öl *(n)* terpentine oil
tertiär tertiary
Tesla-strom *(m)* Tesla current
theoretisch theoretical
thermisch thermal

Thermodiffusion *(f)* thermal diffusion
thermodynamisch thermodynamic
thermogravimetrisch thermogravimetric
tief low, deep
  tiefer lower
tiefblau deep blue
tiefbraun deep brown
Tier *(n)* animal
tierisch(er) (Herkunft) (of) animal (origin)
titriert titrated
titrimetrisch titrimetric(al)
Tl. = **Teil** *(m)* part
Toluol *(n)* toluene
Tonerde *(f)* clay, alumina
Ton-scherbe *(f)* piece of broken pot (baked, fired clay)
Torf *(m)* bituminous peat, turf
Torf-teer *(m)* peat tar
toxisch toxic
Träger *(m)* **(substanz)** *(f)* support, carrier (substance)
Trägheits-moment *(n)* moment of inertia
Traubensäure *(f)* racemic (paratartaric) acid
Trauben-zucker *(m)* dextrose, (D)-glucose
Trennung *(f)* separation

triklin triclinic
Tripelpunkt *(m)* triple-point
Tripelpunkts-druck *(m)* triple-point pressure
tritt ... auf appears
trocken dry
trocknen to dry
Tropfen *(m)* drop

Tropfen-zahl *(f)* drop count
Tropf-zündpunkt *(m)* (droplet) ignition point (temperature)
tropisch tropical
trüb turbid, cloudy, dim (light)
trüben to cloud, go (make) turbid

U

übel sick, ill
über over, above, on, about (a subject)
  Angabe über statement (data) on, about
  über 100° over (above) 100°
Überdruck *(m)* excess, (over-) pressure
überführbar transferable, convertible
überführen (in) to transfer (in) to, convert (in)to
  übergeführt transformed
Überführung *(f)* transformation
Überführungs-zahl *(f)* transference (transport) number
Übergang *(m)* transition, conversion
Übergangs-moment *(n)* transition moment
Übergangs-wahrscheinlichkeit *(f)* transition probability

übergehen (in) to be converted (in)to, pass over (in)to, change (in)to
  geht ... über is converted (in)to
überhitzt superheated, overheated
überlebend surviving
Übersättigung *(f)* supersaturation, over-saturation
Überschuss *(m)* **(an)** excess (of)
überschüssig excess, remaining
Übersicht *(f)* review, survey
übertragen to transfer
Übertragung *(f)* transfer
überwiegend predominant(ly)
überzählig surplus, supernumerary
üblich usual
übrig remaining, residual
Ultramikroskopie *(f)* ultramicroscopy

Ultraschall *(m)* ultrasound, supersonic

Ultraschall-feld *(n)* ultrasonic field

Ultraviolett-bestrahlung *(f)* ultraviolet irradiation

um (a)round, about
  um . . . zu in order to (+ infinitive)

Umesterung *(f)* transesterification

umgekehrt inverted, reverse, inverse(ly)

umgeschlagen (color) changed, converted (in)to

umkristallisieren to recrystallise

Umlagerung *(f)* rearrangement

Umorientierung *(f)* reorientation

Umsatz *(m)* conversion, double decomposition, turnover

Umsetzung *(f)* conversion

umwandeln to convert, transform

Umwandlung *(f)* conversion, transformation

Umwandlungs-enthalpie *(f)* transition, transformation enthalpy

Umwandlungs-entropie *(f)* transition, transformation entropy

Umwandlungs-punkt *(m)* transition (transformation) point

un- negation prefix (cf. adjectives and adverbs without prefix)

unabhängig independent(ly)

unbedeutend insignificant

unbegrenzt unlimited(ly)

unbekannt unknown

unbeschränkt unlimited(ly), unconditional(ly)

unbeständig unstable

und and

undeutlich indistinct, unclear (meaning), unsharp

unerlässlich indispensible

unerwartet unexpected

ungefähr about, approximate(ly)

ungenau inexact, inaccurate

ungesättigt unsaturated

ungewiss uncertain, doubtful

unglasiert unglazed

unklar unclear, indistinct

unkorr. = unkorrigiert uncorrected

unlöslich insoluble

unmittelbar direct(ly), immediate(ly)

unrein impure

unscharf unsharp

unschmelzbar infusible

unten below, under (neath)

unter with, under, among
  unter Bildung von with for-

mation of, leading to formation of

unter Entfernen with removal (separation)

unter Vorbehalt with reservation

unter Zusatz von with addition of

unter 0° below 0°

unterdrücken to suppress

unterhalb below, ben eath

Unterkühlbarkeit *(f)* subcoolability

unterkühlt undercooled, subcooled

Unterkühlung *(f)* undercooling

unter Kühlung with cooling

unterscheiden to distinguish

Unterscheidung *(f)* distinction, discrimination

Unterschied *(m)* difference, distinction

unterschiedlich different(ly), diverse(ly)

untersuchen examine, to investigate, study

untersucht investigated, studied, examined

Untersuchung *(f)* investigation, study, examination

ununterbrochen uninterrupted(ly)

unverändert unchanged

unverd. = **unverdünnt** undiluted

unverzweigt unbranched

unvollständig incomplete(ly)

unwirksam ineffective(ly)

unzersetzt undecomposed

unzutreffend inapplicable, incorrect

Ursprung *(m)* origin

ursprünglich original(ly)

Urteer *(m)* crude tar

UV-Licht *(n)* UV-light

V

Valenz-schwingung *(f)* stretching vibration

Valenz-schwingungs-bande *(f)* stretching vibration band

Valenz-winkel *(m)* (valence) bond angle

vegetabilisch vegetable

Verabreichung *(f)* administration (medicines etc.)

verändern to change

Veränderung *(f)* change

Verarbeitung *(f)* processing, working (up), treatment

Verband (Wund) *(m)* bandage, dressing (wound)

verbessern to improve

Verbindung *(f)* compound, connection, union, joint
Verbrauch *(m)* consumption
verbrauchen to consume
Verbrennung *(f)* combustion
Verbrennungs-enthalpie *(f)* enthalpy of combustion
Verbrennungs-geschwindigkeit *(f)* rate of combustion
Verbrennungs-wärme *(f)* heat of combustion
verbunden connected, joined, bound
verdampfen to evaporate, vaporize
Verdampfung *(f)* evaporation, vaporization
Verdampfungs-enthalpie *(f)* enthalpy of vaporization
Verdampfungs-geschwindigkeit *(f)* rate of vaporization (evaporation)
Verdrängung *(f)* displacement
verd. = verdünnt diluted
verdünnen to dilute
Verdünnung *(f)* dilution
Verdünnungs-enthalpie *(f)* enthalpy of dilution
Verdünnungs-konstante *(f)* dilution constant, factor
Verdünnungs-mittel *(n)* diluent
verdunsten to evaporate
vereinigen to join, combine, bring together, unite
Veresterung *(f)* esterification
Verfahren *(n)* procedure, process, method
verfärben to change color, discolor, fade
verflüchtigen to volatilize
Verfütterung *(f)* feeding
vergären to ferment
vergoren fermented
Vergärung *(f)* fermentation
Vergiftung *(f)* poisoning, contamination
vergleichen to compare
verhalten to behave
Verhalten *(n)* behavior
Verhältnis *(n)* ratio, relation, proportion
verhältnismässig relative(ly)
Verkohlung *(f)* carbonization, charring
verkupfert copper plated (coated)
verlangsamen to slow (down)
Verlauf *(m)* course (of curve, line, process etc.), lapse (time)
verlaufen to proceed, take place, follow a course
verläuft proceeds
Verlust *(m)* loss
vermahlen to grind, pulverize
Vermeidung *(f)* avoidance
vermeintlich supposed
vermindern to reduce, diminish
Verminderung *(f)* reduction, decrease
vermischen to mix
Vermischen (beim) *(n)* on mixing

vermutlich probable, probably, presumable, presumably
verpuffen to deflagrate
verreiben to rub (to a powder), triturate
verringern to reduce, diminish
verrühren to stir
Verschiebung *(f)* shift, displacement
verschieden different(ly), variously
verschmelzen to fuse, melt
versehen (mit) provided (with), equipped (with)
versehentlich inadvertently
verseifen to saponify, hydrolyse under alkaline conditions
verseift saponified, hydrolysed under alkaline conditions
Verseifung *(f)* saponification, alkaline hydrolysis
versetzen to add, mix
beim Versetzen mit on addition of, on mixing with
versetzt mit mixed with
Versuch *(m)* experiment, trial
versuchen to try
verteilen to distribute, disperse
Verteilung *(f)* distribution
Verwechslung *(f)* confusion, mixing up
Verweilzeit *(f)* delay time, retention time
verwenden to use, apply

Verwendung *(f)* use, application
verwittern to weather, effloresce
Verzeichnis *(n)* list, index, register
verzögern to delay, retard
Verzögerung *(f)* delay, retardation
verzweigt branched
vgl. = vergleiche cf. (compare)
viel much, many
vielleicht perhaps
vielmehr rather, more
vier four
violett violet
violettrot violet-red
violettstichig violet-tinged
Virial-koeffizient *(m)* Virial coefficient
Viscosität *(f)* viscosity
voll full
vollständig complete(ly)
vollziehen to put into effect, carry out, accomplish
Volumen *(n)* volume
Volumen-änderung *(f)* volume(tric) change
Volumen-viscosität *(f)* bulk viscosity
vom of the, from the
von of, from
vor before, in front of, ago
vor allem first of all, especially, above all
vorangehend preceding

Vorbehalt *(m)* reservation, restriction
vorbehandeln to pretreat
vorgelegen existed, (was, were) available
vorhanden existing, available, on (at) hand
vorheizen to preheat
vorgeheizt preheated
vorig preceding, previous, former
vorkommen to occur
kommt . . . vor occurs
Vorkommen *(n)* occurrence
Vorlage *(f)* receiver (distillation), original (document)
vorliegen to exist, be present, be available

vorschlagen to propose, suggest
Vorschrift *(f)* prescribed (standardized) method (composition etc.), direction(s), instruction(s), regulation(s)
Vorsicht *(f)* care, (pre)caution
vorsichtig cautious(ly), careful(ly)
vorteilhaft advantageous, favorable
vorübergehend temporary, temporarily, transient(ly)
vorwiegend predominant(ly)
vorzugsweise preferably
Vulkanisations-beschleuniger *(m)* vulcanization accelerator

W. = Wasser *(n)* water
Wachs *(n)* wax
wachsartig waxy, wax-like
Wachstum *(n)* growth, increase
wachstumsfähig capable of growth
Wägung *(f)* weighing
wahr real, true
wahrscheinlich probable, probably
Wahrscheinlichkeit *(f)* probability

wandeln to convert, transform, change
wandern to migrate
warm warm, hot
Wärme *(f)* heat, warmth
Wärme-kapazität *(f)* heat capacity
Wärme-leitfähigkeit *(f)* thermal conductivity
Wärme-quelle *(f)* heat source
Wärme-tönung *(f)* heat tone
Wärme-transport *(m)* heat transport (transfer)

Wärme-übergangs-koeffizient
(m) heat transfer coefficient
waschen to wash
Waschmittel *(n)* detergent, washing agent
Wasser *(n)* water
Wasser-bad *(n)* water-bath
Wasser-dampf *(m)* steam
Wasser-dampf-destillation *(f)* steam distillation
wasserentziehend dehydrating
wasserfrei anhydrous
Wasser-gehalt *(m)* water content
wasserhaltig aqueous, containing water, hydrated
Wasserstoff *(m)* hydrogen
Wasserstoff-abstraktion *(f)* hydrogen abstraction
Wasserstoff-brücke *(f)* hydrogen bridge
Wasserstoff-brücken-bindung *(f)* hydrogen bond
Wasserstoff-peroxid *(n)* hydrogen peroxide
Wasserstoff-strom *(m)* current of hydrogen
Wasser-strom *(m)* current of water
wässrig aqueous
wechseln to change, alternate
wechselnd changing, alternating
Wechselstrom *(m)* alternating current

Wechselwirkung *(f)* interaction
Weg *(m)* way, route, method
wegen because of
Weichmacher *(m)* plasticiser
Wein *(m)* wine
weinrot wine-red
Weinsäure *(f)* tartaric acid
Weise *(f)* manner, way
weiss white
weiter(e) further, additional
weitgehend largely, to a large extent, far reaching
Weizen-kleie *(f)* wheat bran
Weizen-mehl *(n)* wheat flour
Welle *(f)* wave
Wellen-länge *(f)* wave length
Wellen-längenbereich *(m)* wavelength range
Wellen-zahl *(f)* wave number
wenig little, few
wenn if, when
werden (to) become, are (with past participle), will (with infinitive)
  wird becomes, is (with past participle), will (with infinitive)
  (ge)worden (has, have) been (with past participle)
Wert *(m)* value
Wertigkeit *(f)* valency
wertvoll valuable
wesentlich essential(ly), substantial(ly)
wichtig important

Wichtigkeit *(f)* importance
widersprüchlich contradictory
Widerstand *(m)* resistance
widerwärtig unpleasant, disagreeable, objectionable
wiederholt repeated(ly)
Wiederholung *(f)* repetition, recurrence
Winkel *(m)* angle
Wirksamkeit *(f)* effectiveness, efficiency

Wirkung *(f)* effect
Wirkungs-querschnitt *(m)* cross-section
Wismut *(n)* bismuth
Woche *(f)* week
Wolfram *(n)* tungsten
Wolle *(f)* wool
wss. = **wässrig** aq. = aqueous
Wurzel *(f)* root

Z

Zahl *(f)* number, numeral
zahlreich numerous
z. B. = **zum Beispiel** e. g. = for example
zehn ten
Zeile *(f)* line, row
Zeit *(f)* time
zeitlicher Verlauf *(m)* time dependent course, progress (of a reaction etc.)
zellfrei cell-free
Zentral-nerven-system *(n)* central nervous system
zentrifugieren to centrifuge
zerfliessen to deliquesce, fuse together, melt
zerfliesslich deliquescent
zersetzen (sich) to decompose
Zers. = **Zersetzung** *(f)* decomposition

Zers.-temperatur *(f)* decomposition temperature
zersetzlich unstable, liable to decompose, decomposable
Zersetzungs-punkt *(m)* decomposition point
ziegelrot brick-red
ziehen to draw, pull
  in Betracht ziehen to consider
Ziffer *(f)* digit, figure
Zigaretten-rauch *(m)* cigarette smoke
Zimmer-temperatur *(f)* room temperature
Zimtsäure *(f)* cinnamic acid
Zink *(n)* zinc
Zink-staub *(m)* zinc dust
Zinn *(n)* tin
zit. bei = **zitiert bei** cited in

Zonen-schmelzen *(n)* zone refining

zu to, at

Zucker *(m)* sugar

Zuckersäure *(f)* saccharic acid

Zucker-inversion *(f)* inversion of sugar(s)

Zucker-kalk *(m)* sugar-lime, saccharated lime

zuerst initially, firstly

zufügen to add

Zugabe *(f)* addition

zugänglich accessible, approachable

zugeordnet assigned (to), associated (with)

zugleich at the same time

zukommen to relate (pertain) to, belong to, correspond to
diese Formel kommt (dem(r)) ... zu this formula relates to

zuletzt finally, at last

zum Teil partly, partially

Zunahme *(f)* increase

Zündung *(f)* ignition

zuordnen to assign (to), associate, correlate (with)
ist auf Grund (von) ... zugeordnet worden has been assigned on the basis of ...

Zuordnung *(f)* assignment, association, correlation

zur to the

zurücktreten to recede, retire

zusammen (mit) together (with)

zusammenbacken to stick together

zusammenfassen to summarize, collect
zusammenfassende Darstellung *(f)* summary, survey, review

Zusammenfassung *(f)* summary, recapitulation

Zusammensetzung *(f)* composition

zusammengeschmolzen fused together

Zusammentritt *(m)* coming together, coincidence

Zusatz *(m)* addition, additive
unter Zusatz von with addition of

zusätzlich additional(ly)

zuschreiben to attribute to, assign, ascribe

Zustand *(m)* state, condition

Zustands-diagramm *(n)* phase diagram

Zustands-gleichung *(f)* equation of state

Zustands-grösse *(f)* state function

zutreffend relevant, correct

Zutritt *(m)* ingress, admittance, entry

zuvor beforehand, previously

zwanzig twenty

(und) zwar (and) particularly, namely, no doubt
Zweck *(m)* purpose
zweckmässig suitable, expedient, practical
zwecks for the purpose of
zwei two
zweifach twofold
zweimal (zwei Mal) twice
zweifelhaft doubtful

zweite(r) second
zweites Moment *(n)* second moment
zwischen between
Zwischenprodukt *(n)* intermediate
Zwischenstufe *(f)* intermediate step, stage
zwölf twelve
Zylinder *(m)* cylinder

Formulations commonly used in Beilstein

A. Constitution

(1) **Die früher unter dieser Konstitution beschriebene Verbindung ist (wahrscheinlich) als . . . . zu formulieren.** The compound formerly described by this constitution is to be (probably) formulated as . . . .

(2) **Entsprechendes gilt für die als . . . und als . . . beschriebenen Derivate.** Correspondingly for the derivatives described as . . . and as . . .

(3) **Bezüglich der Konstitution s. . . .** For the constitution see . . .

(4) **Die(se) (beiden) Konstitution(en)** (Both) the(se) constitution(s)
— **wird (werden) auf Grund der genetischen Beziehung zu . . .**
— **zugeordnet.** — is (are) assigned on the basis of their derivational relationship to . . .
— **wird (werden) der (den) nachstehenden Verbindung(en) zugeordnet.** — is (are) assigned to the following compound(s).
— **kommt (wahrscheinlich) der von . . . als . . . formulierten Verbindung zu.** — is (probably) assignable to the compound formulated as . . . by . . .

(5) **Nach Ausweis des . . .-Spektrums** According to the . . . spectrum
— **liegt (bei Raumtemperatur) überwiegend . . . vor.** — . . . predominates (at room temperature).
— **hat im nachstehend beschriebenen Präparat . . . vorgelegen.** — compound . . . was present in the described next.

59

(6) **Die Verbindung ist als ... zu formulieren.** The compound is to be formulated as ...

(7) **Außer dieser Konstitution ist auch die Formulierung als ... in Betracht zu ziehen.** Besides this constitution the formulation ... must also be considered.

(8) **Über eine ebenfalls unter dieser Konstitution beschriebene Verbindung s. ...** For a further compound described by this constitution see ...

(9) **Die Konstitution ist nicht gesichert.** This constitution has not been fully verified.

(10) **Die Einheitlichkeit ist zweifelhaft.** The homogeneity is doubtful.

(11) **Die Identität der von ... unter dieser Konstitution beschriebenen Verbindung ist ungewiss.** The identity of the compound described by ... as having this constitution is uncertain.

(12) **In dem in ... beschriebenen Präparat** In the compound described in ...
— **hat ein Gemisch von ... mit ... vorgelegen.** — a mixture of ... and ... was present.
— **hat ein Gemisch mit dem unter ... beschriebenen Stereoisomeren vorgelegen.** — a mixture containing the stereoisomers described in ... was present.
— **hat ein Isomerengemisch vorgelegen.** — a mixture of isomers was present.

B. Isolation

(1) **Gewinnung aus dem unter ... beschriebenen Racemat mit Hilfe von ...** Isolation from the racemate described under ... with the aid of ...

(2) **Gewinnung aus gleichen Teilen der unter a) und b) beschriebenen optischen Antipoden.** Isolation from equal parts of the optical antipodes described under a) and b)

C. Formation (abbreviated B.)

(1) Aus . . . mit Hilfe von . . .   From . . . with the aid of . . .

(2) Aus . . . beim Behandeln*) mit . . . und anschliessenden Behandeln*) mit . . .   From . . . on treatment* with . . . and subsequent treatment*) with . . .

(3) Aus . . . bei der Umsetzung mit . . . und anschließendem Behandeln*) mit . . .   From . . . by conversion with . . . and subsequent treatment*) with . . .

(4) Analog (aus) der vorangehenden (folgenden) Verbindung.   Analogous to the preceding (following) compound.

(5) s. im vorangehenden/voranstehenden (folgenden) Artikel.   See preceding (following) item.

D. Chemical behavior

(1) Beim Behandeln*) mit . . . ist . . . erhalten worden.   Treatment*) with . . . results in formation of . . .

(2) Bildung von . . . und . . . beim Behandeln*) mit . . . in . . . unter Zusatz von . . . und Behandeln*) des Reaktionsprodukts mit . . .   Formation of . . . and . . . on treatment*) with . . . in . . . with addition of . . . and treatment*) of the reaction product with . . .

(3) Beim Erhitzen mit . . . in . . . auf . . .°, anschliessenden Behandeln*) mit . . . und Erhitzen des danach erhaltenen Reaktionsprodukts auf . . .° ist . . . erhalten worden.   Heating with in . . . to . . .°, subsequent treatment*) with . . . and heating the reaction product obtained to . . .° results in . . .

(4) Mengenverhältnis der Reaktionsprodukte . . . und . . . beim Behandeln*) mit . . . bei . . .°.   Ratio of reaction products . . . and . . . on treatment*) with . . . at . . .°.

---

*) For possible alternative wording consult dictionary.

(5) **Gleichgewichtskonstante des Reaktionssystems** ... Equilibrium constant of the reaction system ...

(6) **Kinetik der Reaktion mit** ... Kinetics of the reaction with ...
Geschwindigkeitskonstante der Reaktion mit ... Rate constant of the reaction with ...
Zeitlicher Verlauf der Reaktion mit ... Time dependent progress of the reaction with ...

(7) **Reaktivität gegenüber** ... Reactivity towards ...

(8) **Analog verlaufen die Reaktionen der Homologen.** The reactions of the homologs proceed analogously.

(9) **Die beim Behandeln*) mit** ... **erhaltene Verbindung** The compound obtained on treatment with ...
— **ist als** ... **zu formulieren.** — is formulated as ...
— **ist nicht als** ..., **sondern als** ... **zu formulieren.** — is not formulated as ... but as ...

(10) **Die Identität der beim Behandeln*) mit** ... **erhaltenen, früher als** ... **beschriebenen Verbindung ist ungewiss.** The identity of the compound obtained on treatment*) with ..., formerly described as ... is uncertain.

(11) **Beim Behandeln*) mit** ... **ist** ... **nicht wiedererhalten worden.** ... is not recovered by treatment with ...

---

*) For possible alternative wording consult dictionary.

A brand new Poster
for your organic department:

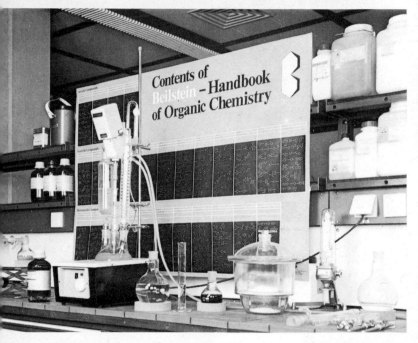

The Beilstein Reference Chart

This poster was developed by scientists for scientists, and contains
a wealth of usefull information for the user of the Beilstein Handbook
of Organic Chemistry.
The Beilstein Handbook (handbook of carbon compounds) is, as you
know, an internationally recognised standard work, widely used in
all branches of chemistry and related fields.
Please send your request for a free copy.

Do You Know How To Make The Best Use Of This Standard Work Of Chemistry?

How to use Beilstein ...

Beilstein Handbook of Organic Chemistry

The new guideline 'How to use Beilstein' offers valuable help here. This concise and readable booklet provides all the information necessary to locate a particular item in Beilstein in the shortest possible time.

The guideline is also published in German and Japanese.

Please send your request for a free copy.